Apple On The Bed

Written by Susheila Stone
Illustrated by Rob Englebright

Collins Educational
An imprint of HarperCollins*Publishers*

A a

B b

apple on the **b**ed

cat on the **d**esk

Ee Ff

egg on a fork

Gg Hh

girl on a **h**orse

insects in the jug

Kk Ll

key in the **l**ock

Mm Nn

mouse in a **n**et

Oo Pp

orange on a **p**late

queen in her robe

Ss Tt

snake in the **t**ree

umbrella in the **v**an

wig in a box

Yy Zz

yak in a zoo

a
b
c
d
e
f
g
h
i
j
k
l

m n o p
q r s t
u v w x
y z